ANTHOLOGY

RICHARD RODGERS

*R*2002™

CENTENARY

Photos and Biography courtesy of Rodgers & Hammerstein Organization

Thanks to the publishers:
CAFÉ CONCERTO s.r.l. - Milano
Edizioni CHAPPELL s.r.l. - Milano
WARNER BROS. PUBLICATIONS U.S. Inc.
Edizioni CURCI s.r.l. - Milano

special thanks to:

Richard Rodger & Lorenz Hart

BIOGRAPHY

Richard Rodgers' contributions to the musical theatre of his day were extraordinary, and his influence on the musical theatre of today and tomorrow is legendary. His career spanned more than six decades, and his hits ranged from the silver screens of Hollywood to the bright lights of Broadway, London and beyond. He was the recipient of countless awards, including Pulitzers, Tonys, Oscars, Grammys and Emmys. He wrote more than 900 published songs, and forty Broadway musicals.

Richard Charles Rodgers was born in New York City on June 28, 1902. His earliest professional credits, beginning in 1920, included a series of musicals for Broadway, London and Hollywood written exclusively with lyricist Lorenz Hart. In the first decade of their collaboration, Rodgers & Hart averaged two new shows every season, beginning with **POOR LITTLE RITZ GIRL**, and also including **THE GARRICK GAIETIES** (of 1925 and 1926), **DEAREST ENEMY, PEGGY-ANN**, **A CONNECTICUT YANKEE** and **CHEE-CHEE**. After spending the years 1931 to 1935 in Hollywood (where they wrote the scores for several feature films including **LOVE ME TONIGHT** starring Maurice Chevalier, **HALLELUJAH, I'M A BUM** starring Al Jolson and **THE PHANTOM PRESIDENT** starring George M. Cohan), they returned to New York to compose the score for Billy Rose's circus extravaganza, **JUMBO**.

A golden period followed — golden for Rodgers & Hart, and golden for the American musical: **ON YOUR TOES** (1936), **BABES IN ARMS** (1937), **I'D RATHER BE RIGHT** (1937), **I MARRIED AN ANGEL** (1938), **THE BOYS FROM SYRACUSE** (1938), **TOO MANY GIRLS** (1939), **HIGHER AND HIGHER** (1940), **PAL JOEY** (1940), and **BY JUPITER** (1942). The Rodgers & Hart partnership came to an end with the death of Lorenz Hart in 1943, at the age of 48.

Earlier that year Rodgers had joined forces with lyricist and author Oscar Hammerstein II, whose work in the field of operetta throughout the '20s and '30s had been as innovative as Rodgers' own accomplishments in the field of musical comedy. **OKLAHOMA!** (1943), the first Rodgers & Hammerstein musical, was also the first of a new genre, the musical play, representing a unique fusion of Rodgers' musical comedy and Hammerstein's operetta. A milestone in the development of the American musical, it also marked the beginning of the most successful partnership in Broadway musical history, and was followed by **CAROUSEL** (1945), **ALLEGRO** (1947), **SOUTH PACIFIC** (1949), **THE KING AND I** (1951), **ME AND JULIET** (1953), **PIPE DREAM** (1955), **FLOWER DRUM SONG** (1958) and **THE SOUND OF MUSIC** (1959). The team wrote one movie musical, STATE FAIR (1945), and one for television, **CINDERELLA**. (1957). Collectively, the Rodgers & Hammerstein musicals earned 34 Tony Awards, 15 Academy Awards, two Pulitzer Prizes, two Grammy Awards and 2 Emmy Awards. In 1998 Rodgers & Hammerstein were cited by Time Magazine and CBS News as among the 20 most influential artists of the 20th century and in 1999 they were jointly commemorated on a U.S. postage stamp. Despite Hammerstein's death in 1960, Rodgers continued to write for the Broadway stage. His first solo entry, **NO STRINGS** in 1962, earned him two Tony Awards for music and lyrics, and was followed by **DO I HEAR A WALTZ?** (1965, lyrics by Stephen Sondheim), **TWO BY TWO** (1970, lyrics by Martin Charnin), **REX** (1976, lyrics by Sheldon Harnick) and **I REMEMBER MAMA** (1979, lyrics by Martin Charnin and Raymond Jessel).

NO STRINGS was not the only project for which Rodgers worked solo: as composer/lyricist he wrote the score for a 1967 television adaptation of Bernard Shaw's **ANDROCLES AND THE LION** for NBC; contributed songs to a 1962 remake of **STATE FAIR**; and to the 1965 movie version of **THE SOUND OF MUSIC**. He composed one ballet score (**GHOST TOWN**, premiered in 1939), and two television documentary scores — **VICTORY AT SEA** in 1952 and **THE VALIANT YEARS** in 1960 (the former earning him an Emmy, a Gold Record and a commendation from the U.S. Navy.)

Richard Rodgers died at home in New York City on December 30, 1979 at the age of 77. On March 27, 1990, he was honored posthumously with Broadway's highest accolade when the 46th Street Theatre, owned and operated by the Nederlander Organization, was renamed The Richard Rodgers Theatre, home to The Richard Rodgers Gallery, a permanent exhibit in the lobby areas presented by ASCAP which honors the composer's life and works.

Richard Rodger & Oscar Hammerstein II

Richard Rodger & Lorenz Hart

Richard Rodger & Lorenz Hart

from "Pal Joey" - 1941

BEWITCHED

Words by Lorenz Hart - Music by Richard Rodgers

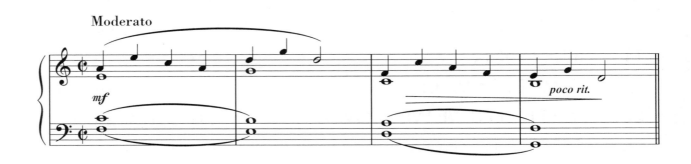

VERSE
(not fast)

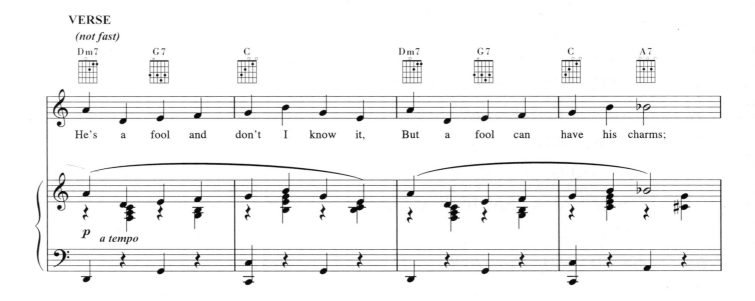

He's a fool and don't I know it, But a fool can have his charms;

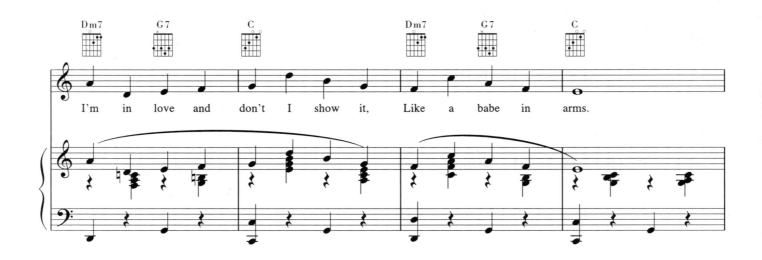

I'm in love and don't I show it, Like a babe in arms.

from "South Pacific" - 1949

BALI HA'I

Words by Oscar Hammerstein II - Music by Richard Rodgers

You'll hear me call you, Sing - ing through the sun - shine, Sweet and

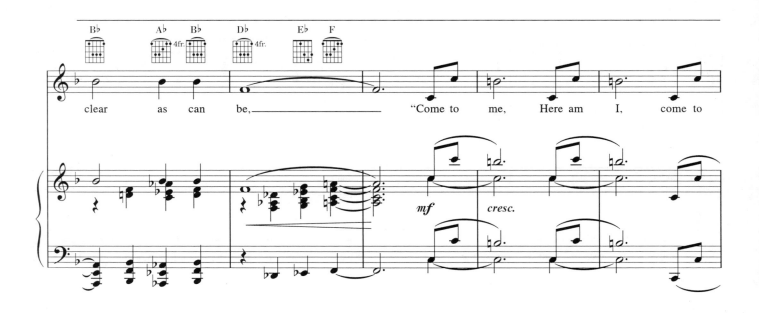

clear as can be,_____ "Come to me, Here am I, come to

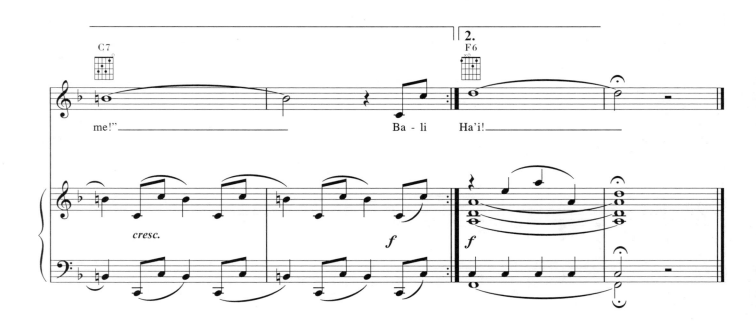

me!"_____ Ba - li Ha'i!_____

BLUE MOON

Words by Lorenz Hart - Music by Richard Rodgers

12

14

15

from "The Sound Of Music" - 1959

CLIMB EV'RY MOUNTAIN

Words by Oscar Hammerstein II - Music by Richard Rodgers

18

Climb ev - 'ry moun - tain, ford ev - 'ry stream,

allargando

f legato

Fol - low ev - 'ry rain - bow, till you find your

più cresc. e poco a poco allarg.

ff

1.

dream!

2.

dream!

f

ff marcato

from "Pal Joey" - 1941

I COULD WRITE A BOOK

Words by Lorenz Hart - Music by Richard Rodgers

got.   I won't waste a - ny   time,   I'll   strike while the i - ron is   hot.   If they

asked   me,   I could write a   book,_____ a - bout the   way you walk and

whis-per,   and   look._____   I could   write   a   pre-face   on

how   we   met,   so   the   world   would   ne - ver   for -

from "The Boys From Syracuse" - 1938

FALLING IN LOVE WITH LOVE

Words by Lorenz Hart - Music by Richard Rodgers

25

from "The King And I" - 1951

GETTING TO KNOW YOU

Words by Oscar Hammerstein II - Music by Richard Rodgers

It's a ver-y an-cient say-ing But a true and hon-est thought, That if you be-come a teach-er, by your pu-pils you'll be taught. As a teach-er, I've been

from "The King And I" - 1951

HELLO, YOUNG LOVERS

Words by Oscar Hammerstein II - Music by Richard Rodgers

Moderato

When I think of Tom I think a-bout a night When the earth smelled of sum-mer, And the

sky was streaked with white, And the soft mist of Eng-land was sleep-ing on a hill; I re-

34

REFRAIN
(Very moderately)

Hel - lo, young lov - ers, Who - ev - er you are, I hope your trou - bles are few _____ All my good wish - es go with you to - night I've been in love like you _____ Be brave, young lov - ers, and fol - low your

from "Too Many Girls" - 1939

I DIDN'T KNOW WHAT TIME IT WAS

Words by Lorenz Hart - Music by Richard Rodgers

Once I was young, yes-ter-day, per-haps, Danced with Jim and Paul And

kissed some oth-er chaps. Once I was young, but nev-er was na-ive, I

from "Carousel" - 1945

IF I LOVED YOU

Words by Oscar Hammerstein II - Music by Richard Rodgers

from "State Fair" - 1945

IT MIGHT AS WELL BE SPRING

Words by Oscar Hammerstein II - Music by Richard Rodgers

48

from "Higher And Higher" - 1940

IT NEVER ENTERED MY MIND

Words by Lorenz Hart - Music by Richard Rodgers

Moderato

I don't care if there's pow-der on my nose, I don't care if my

p legato e tranquillo

hair-do is in place. I've lost the ver-y mean-ing of re-pose, I

nev-er put a mud pack on my face. Oh, who'd have thought that I'd

from "The Sound Of Music" - 1959

MY FAVORITE THINGS

Words by Oscar Hammerstein II - Music by Richard Rodgers

Rain - drops on ros - es and whisk - ers on kit - tens, Bright cop - per ket - tles and warm wool - en mit - tens, Brown pa - per pack - ag - es

from "Babes In Arms" - 1937

MY FUNNY VALENTINE

Words by Lorenz Hart - Music by Richard Rodgers

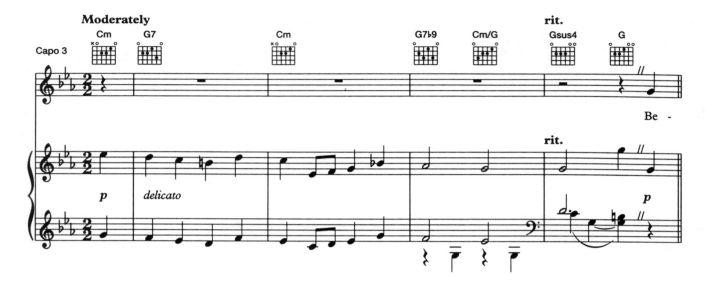

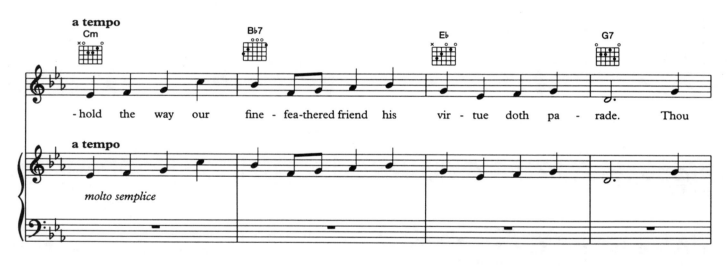

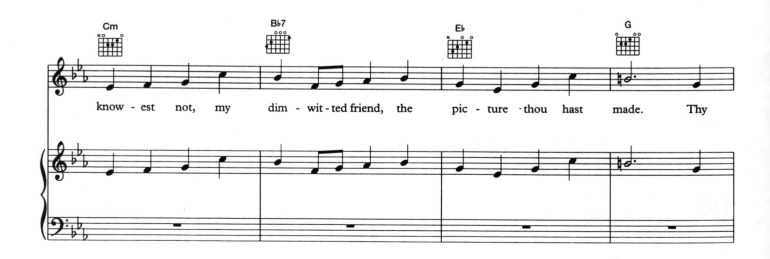

from "Oklahoma!" - 1943

OKLAHOMA

Words by Oscar Hammerstein II - Music by Richard Rodgers

64

from "Oklahoma!" - 1943

PEOPLE WILL SAY WE'RE IN LOVE

Words by Oscar Hammerstein II - Music by Richard Rodgers

1. Why do they think up stor - ies that link my name with yours?_____
2. Some peo - ple claim that you are to blame as much as I_____

Why do the neigh - bors chat - ter all day, be - hind their doors?
Why do you take the troub - le to bake my fav' - - rite pie?

67

from "The King And I" - 1951

SHALL WE DANCE?

Words by Oscar Hammerstein II - Music by Richard Rodgers

oth - er, And shall you be my new ro - mance?_____

_____ On the clear un - der - stand - ing that this

kind of thing can hap - pen, Shall we dance? Shall we dance? Shall we

dance? Shall we dance?_____

from "South Pacific" - 1949

SOME ENCHANTED EVENING

Words by Oscar Hammerstein II - Music by Richard Rodgers

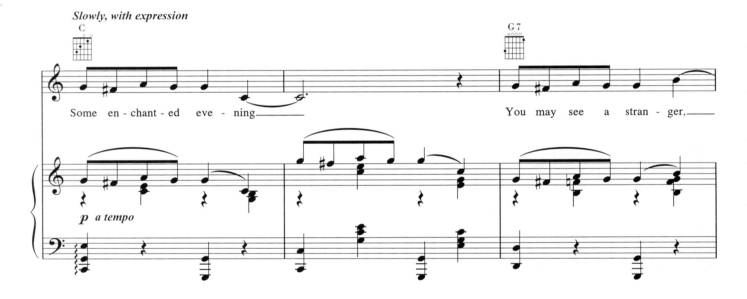

from "Simple Simon" - 1930

TEN CENTS A DANCE

Words by Lorenz Hart - Music by Richard Rodgers

from "Babes In Arms" - 1937

THE LADY IS A TRAMP

Words by Lorenz Hart - Music by Richard Rodgers

from "On Your Toes" - 1936

THERE'S A SMALL HOTEL

Words by Lorenz Hart - Music by Richard Rodgers

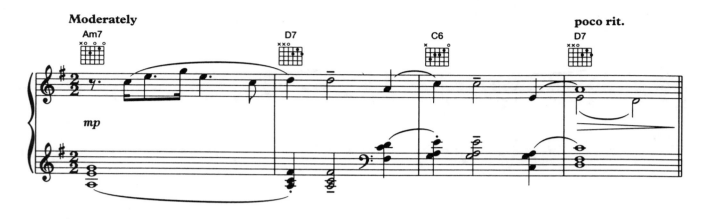

I'd like to get a - way, Jun-ior, some-where a - lone with you.

It could be oh, so gay, Jun-ior! You need a laugh or two.

89

from "Babes In Arms" - 1937

WHERE OR WHEN

Words by Lorenz Hart - Music by Richard Rodgers

In moderate tempo

from "Oklahoma!" - 1943

OH, WHAT A BEAUTIFUL MORNIN'

Words by Oscar Hammerstein II - Music by Richard Rodgers

from "Carousel" - 1945

YOU'LL NEVER WALK ALONE

Words by Oscar Hammerstein II - Music by Richard Rodgers

from "South Pacific" - 1949

YOUNGER THAN SPRINGTIME

Words by Oscar Hammerstein II - Music by Richard Rodgers

Moderato

f espressivo

molto rit.

with warm expression

I touch your hand And my arms grow strong

mp a tempo

Like a pair of birds That burst with song.

INGRAF s.r.l. - Via Monte S. Genesio 7 - Milano
Stampato in Italia - Printed in Italy - Imprimé en Italie 2002